# SADIE

Sue Houchens

PAGE PUBLISHING, INC.
New York, NY

First originally published by Page Publishing, Inc. 2018

ISBN 978-1-68409-627-5 (Paperback)
ISBN 978-1-68409-628-2 (Digital)

Printed in the United States of America

To all the animals finding their forever homes and the humans who make that possible.

Pat–
Another
"Special Friend"
–
Sue

Have *you* ever had a *very special* friend who was always happy with *you* and did what only *you* wanted to do? Did they help clean up *your* spills? Were they always right next to *you*, excited about whatever move *you* might make? Did *you* somehow know that they loved *you* every bit as much as *you* loved them?

If so, then *you* have a *very special friend*!

Sometimes you meet friends in the *strangest* places. That happened to me the day I met Sadie at the animal shelter.

Because she *is* such a special friend, I'd like to share how she came into my life.

I was looking for a smallish type of dog, one that I could easily carry. When I arrived at the shelter, I was informed there were only two dogs for me to consider. I toured the length of the kennel in hopes of finding the right dog for me.

In the kennel, there were large dogs, medium-sized dogs, but only two dogs that were just the right size of *small*.

Walking down the row of cages, I felt sad for all the homeless dogs. It's cold and scary when you're alone. I hoped they could all find their forever homes.

4

I reached the end of the cages. As I turned around and started back to visit my first possibility, my eyes met Sadie's. It was magical. Her eyes were soft and kind. She had such a gentle way about her.

I wasn't going to meet her just yet, but there was a quiet attraction between us when I passed her cage. However, I continued to walk back to the first little dog. She was very sweet and small and had short curly brown hair. Her tail was wagging a mile a minute. I could tell she wanted to meet me.

Just as I was ready to tell Joe, the kennel helper, to get this frisky little pup, I stopped in my tracks and said, "I'd like to visit the other one instead."

Both Joe and I were surprised. What had I just said? The brown dog was so excited, yet I had asked to see the other.

Together we walked back to the quiet kennel, and there she was, proudly sitting. She uttered not one peep. She simply sat and waited for Joe to pick her up and take her to the playroom for a visit.

I sat on the bench thinking about that soft face when Joe put Sadie on the floor. As he left us there alone, he smiled at me and, with a wink of his eye, said, "Enjoy!"

There we were, just the two of us.

I was nervous. Sadie was so little and fluffy. Then, with wide eyes and a hop, a skip, and a jump, she was sitting by my side. She stared at me with those dark, kind eyes, and before I knew it, I was stroking her soft white fur and floppy gray ears.

She was, as I imagined, soft, kind, and gentle. We simply stared at each other. She snuggled up and put her right paw on my leg. Her big, dark eyes made me feel safe. She cocked her head as if to ask, "Are you my friend?" I knew this was the dog I had been looking for.

I don't know how long we sat on that bench, but when I finally said, "O-k-a-y, let's go home," Sadie seemed to smile as if she understood.

She was such a tiny thing, so fragile, yet she calmed me by snuggling in my arms and putting her head on my chest as I carried her to the front desk.

I was concerned that Sadie might get upset when the veterinary assistant injected a special owner chip under her skin. She didn't utter a sound. She seemed to understand that it was important and necessary.

Sadie was quiet all the way home. I wondered what she must be thinking. I knew I was thinking how much I had already fallen in love with her. When we arrived, her sister and brother cats were there to meet her. Sweet girl that she was, Sadie met them with calm confidence. They, on the other hand, greeted her with not-so-welcoming hisses, letting her know they were here first!

It wasn't until months after her adoption that she even gave a soft growl when another dog passed by *her* house.

Sadie has made her way into the hearts of both family and friends. Who can possibly resist that gentle-mannered, fluffy little dog with floppy gray ears and big dark eyes, who seems to know every word you say?

How was I so lucky to have come upon this wonderful companion? How did she get to be five years old and not have a home? Sadly, she can't answer any of my questions. I will never know her past, only her future.

What I did know was that she had been found in a lonely, vacant van in a dark, dusty parking lot. The shelter gave her a bath, which made her clean and fluffy. As she was weak, the veterinarian said Sadie needed good food to help her get strong. He also said she needed a good toothbrushing.

I thank the powers that be for delivering me to that particular animal shelter the very day she was released for adoption.

Sadie has become *My Very Special Friend*!

19

# About the Author

Sue Houchens is a retired elementary school teacher, native to Denver, Colorado. In fact, Sue received her bachelor's degree from Metropolitan State University of Denver and later her master's from Walden University. The human-animal bond was instilled in Sue at a very young age from her family growing up, but her understanding of this bond has deepened over the years.

Sue's husband, Jim, is a practicing small animal veterinarian, who looks to protect the human-animal bond through healing and preventative care for pets. Sue and Jim are blessed with two daughters who also share the love of the many dogs, cats, birds, pocket pets, and fish the family has owned over the years. Sue's special friend, Sadie, continues to live the peaceful coexistence with the family cats Ellie and Harry.

CPSIA information can be obtained
at www.ICGtesting.com
Printed in the USA
LVHW01s2337040418
572218LV00005B/25/P